+MATHS FOR MA[RTIANS]

Galaxy Getaway

Illustrated by Jane Tassie ○ Written by Julie Ferris

KING*f*ISHER

KINGFISHER
Kingfisher Publications Plc,
New Penderel House,
283-288 High Holborn,
London WC1V 7HZ

First published by
Kingfisher Publications Plc 2000
10 9 8 7 6 5 4 3 2 1

1TR/0100/TWP/FR/170ARM

A CIP catalogue record for
this book is available from
the British Library.

ISBN 0 7534 0444 3

Printed in Singapore

Production controllers:
Jacquie Horner,
Caroline Jackson
DTP Co-ordinator:
Nicky Studdart

YOU WILL PROBABLY NEED
TO USE PENCIL AND PAPER
TO HELP YOU SOLVE SOME
OF THE PUZZLES.

Contents

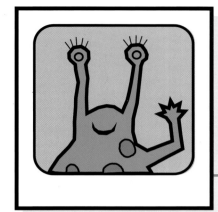

Zeno is only 86 Martian years old (about 10 Earth years). He lives with his mother in Zala, a small city on Mars. Zeno likes adventure, but is not always very brave.

Zormella is Zeno's cyberpal. She lives in Myria City on planet Numis. She is very practical and always carries a purple rucksack full of useful things.

Zarf is a bernum - a small, friendly creature from planet Zib. Bernums are very popular pets throughout the universe.

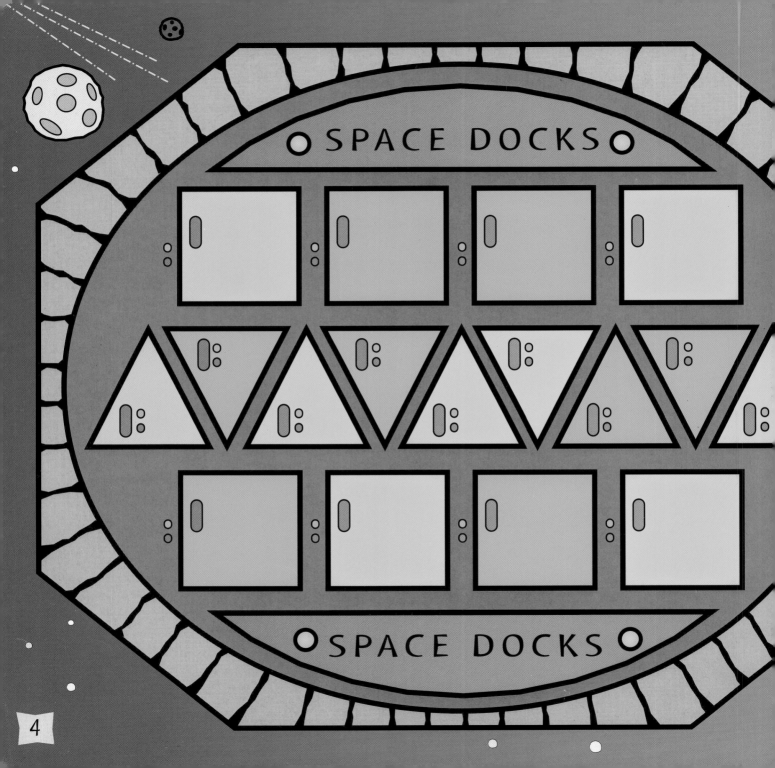

SPACE DOCKS

SPACE DOCKS

4

Testing times

Zeno the Martian is feeling very nervous. Today he is taking his space licence test. He's already flown through a meteor shower and orbited a planet. Now is the hardest part - he has to land his spaceship in a docking port. Can you help him?

SPACE TEST

Martian space docks have square-shaped and triangle-shaped entry pods. The square pods are for space buses and the triangular pods are for smaller craft. Empty space pods have yellow doors. How many space bus pods are empty? Zeno is flying a small craft. How many pods can he use?

SPACE LICENCE

This is to certify that

Zeno the Martian

----

has successfully completed the spacecraft test and is licensed to fly in all sectors of known space.

Zeno

SPACE BUS

On board

To celebrate getting his space licence, Zeno is planning a special space journey. For many Martian years he has sent intergalactic messages to a cyberpal (a little like a space penpal) in a nearby galaxy. His cyberpal, Zormella, has invited Zeno to visit. It is a long journey and Zeno needs to check his spaceship to make sure it is shipshape and ready to fly.

Bedroom

There is a secret safe in the bedroom wall for storing valuables. To find it, look on the wallpaper for a star that looks different. Starting in the top left corner, count across the rows from left to right. What number star is it?

Kitchen

Zeno's favourite drink is barp juice. He usually drinks one carton of barp juice every two hours. The journey will take 12 hours. Does he have enough barp juice?

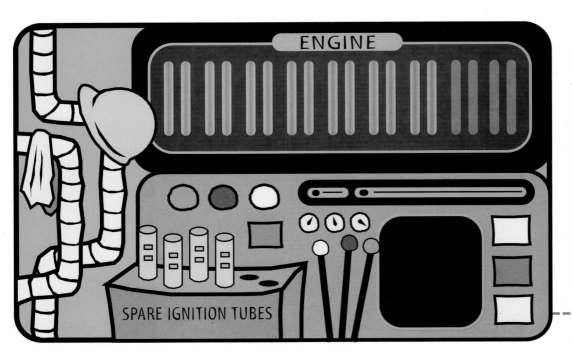

Engine room

The spaceship needs eight ignition tubes to take off. Each ignition tube lights up two bars on the engine's display panel. Are there enough ignition tubes loaded?

Take-off

Zeno's spaceship blasts out of the space dock. He is very excited about visiting his cyberpal. He is also a little worried about flying so far all by himself. There is a lot of traffic in the Martian skies and Zeno gets stuck in a space jam. While he waits he tries to work out what the most popular colour spaceship is. Can you figure it out?

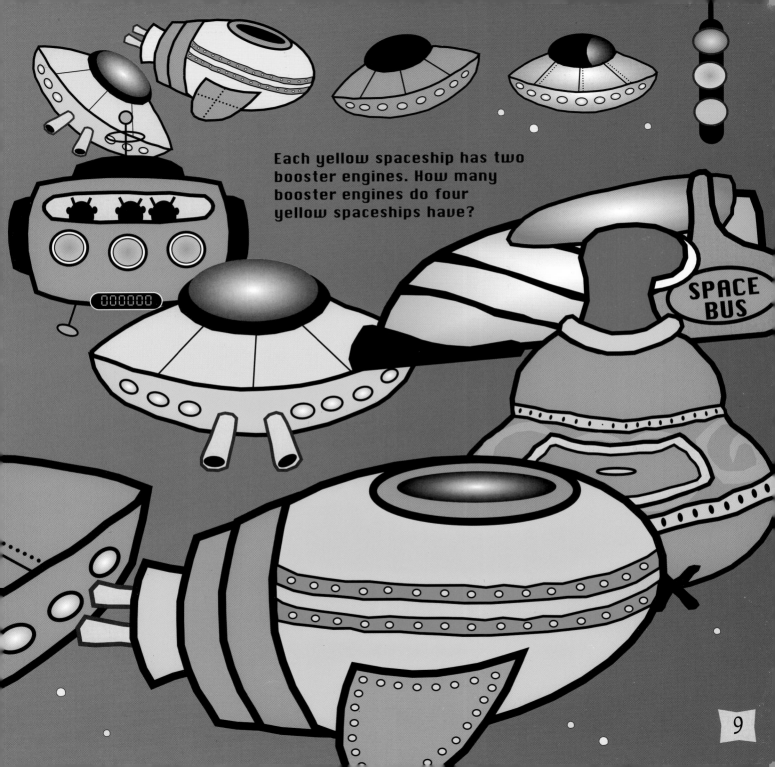

Each yellow spaceship has two booster engines. How many booster engines do four yellow spaceships have?

SPACE BUS

9

Fuel stops

Zeno's spaceship is a real fuel-guzzler. He has to stop for fuel often or he will get stuck in outer space. Only planets that are part of the five times table have fuel supplies. Can you guide Zeno's spaceship across the galaxy?

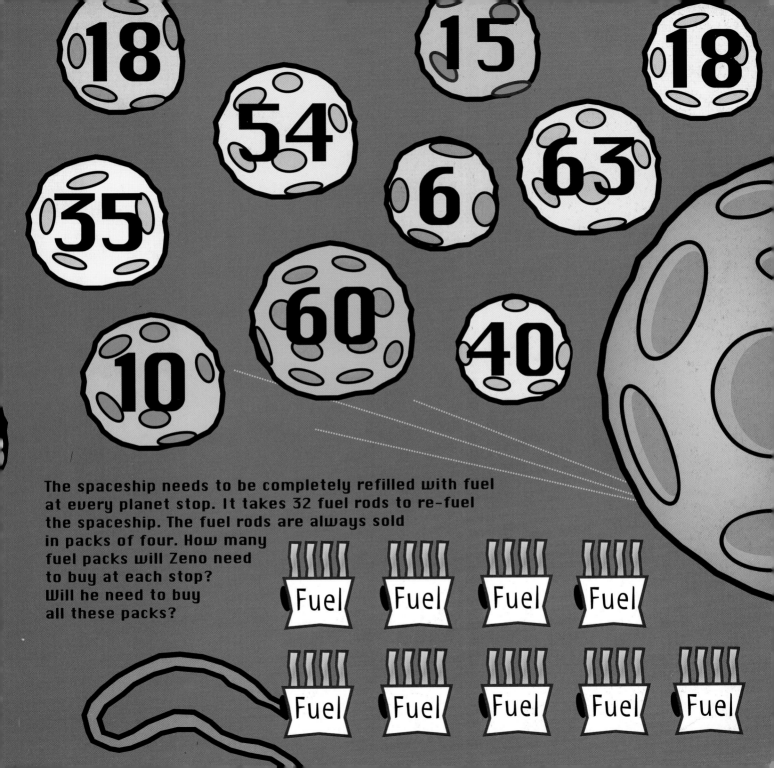

The spaceship needs to be completely refilled with fuel at every planet stop. It takes 32 fuel rods to re-fuel the spaceship. The fuel rods are always sold in packs of four. How many fuel packs will Zeno need to buy at each stop? Will he need to buy all these packs?

Bubble attack

6 15
14
17 8

+
− −
+ −

Zeno is enjoying his space flight through the galaxy. It is great to see new planets and a real adventure to be so far from home. Suddenly, he spots four space bubbles racing towards his spaceship. He has only a few minutes to burst them before he crashes into them!

To burst the bubbles Zeno must empty them of numbers. Can you help him?

Take:
- A number from the first bubble.
- A plus or minus sign from the second bubble.
- A number from the third bubble.
- The correct answer from the fourth bubble.

Do this until the bubbles are empty.

Lunchtime!

Bursting bubbles really builds up an appetite! Zeno's favourite meal is grilled zibbers with mashed space prunes. He is out of zibbers so he has to land on planet Zib to get some. His automatic turbo food sucker has already collected three zibbers. How many more does he need to make his Mum's recipe?

Zibbers are always found in small groups. How many are in each group? How many zibbers are there in total? Can you find enough space prunes for the recipe?

MUM'S RECIPE

Ingredients:

- 17 zibbers
- 10 space prunes
- A pinch of asteroid dust

Lightly grill the zibbers. Boil the space prunes, add a pinch of asteroid dust, and mash. Serve immediately. Enjoy!

Stowaway

As Zeno tucks into his grilled zibbers with mashed space prunes, he hears a strange rustling sound coming from behind the chest of drawers. Zeno is not the bravest alien in the universe and at first he is too scared to investigate. Finally he finds the courage to look. Slowly he peers into the darkness. Something is creeping towards him...

It takes him a few seconds to recognize the strange-looking creature. Then he sees it is just a harmless bernum from the planet Zib. He must have crept aboard while Zeno was collecting zibbers.

Hanging around the bernum's neck is a collar with a small message barrel attached to it. There is a message written in code.

Can you crack the code and read the message?

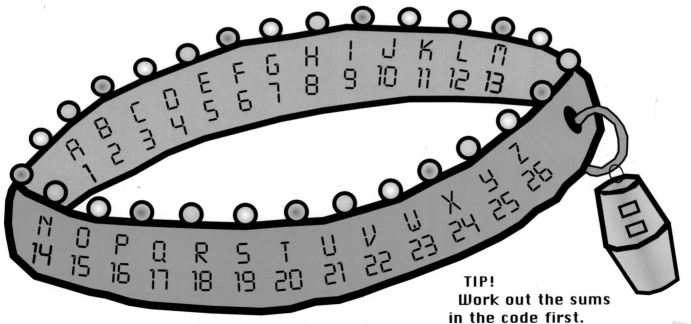

TIP!
Work out the sums
in the code first.

Planet Numis

The bernum is friendly. Zeno has always wanted a pet alien, so he takes Zarf the bernum along on his journey. Soon Zeno can see planet Numis. He can't wait to meet his cyberpal, Zormella. Before he lands, Zeno wants to find out more about planet Numis. Here is what he finds on his spaceship's computer.

Millennium Bug

Zormella xx

City populations on planet Numis

POPULATION

7 million
6 million
5 million
4 million
3 million
2 million
1 million

CITY

Numopolis
Myria
Macro
Argon

Zormella lives in Myria. What is the population of Myria?

Which Numis city has the largest population?

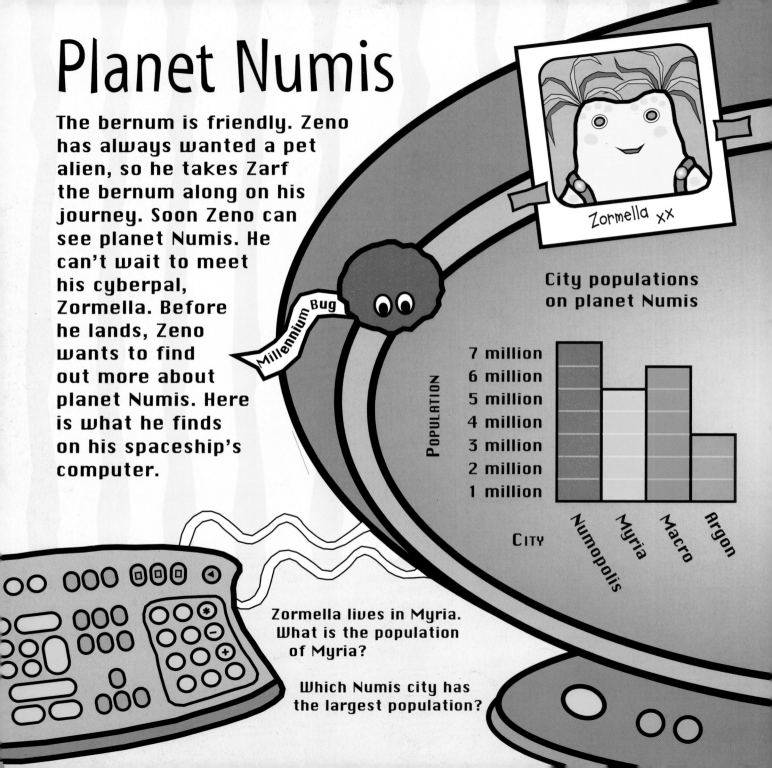

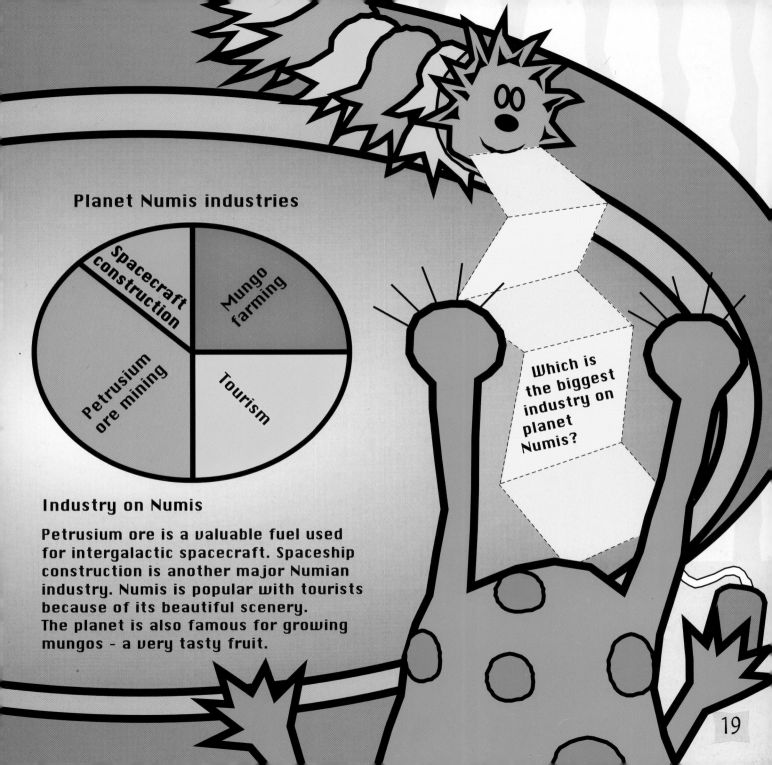

Planet Numis industries

Pie chart with four sections:
- Spacecraft construction
- Mungo farming
- Petrusium ore mining
- Tourism

Industry on Numis

Petrusium ore is a valuable fuel used for intergalactic spacecraft. Spaceship construction is another major Numian industry. Numis is popular with tourists because of its beautiful scenery. The planet is also famous for growing mungos - a very tasty fruit.

Which is the biggest industry on planet Numis?

Sightseeing

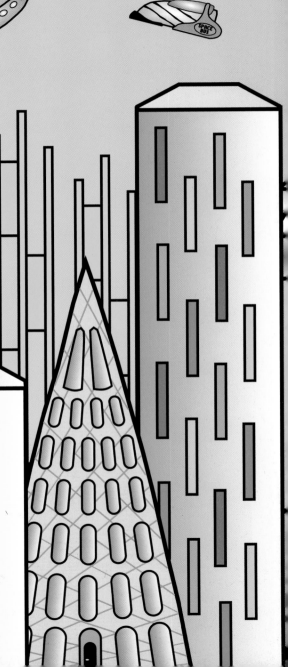

Zeno lands his spaceship in a Numis docking bay. Zormella is waiting for him. She and Zeno are very happy to finally meet each other. Zeno introduces Zormella to Zarf and the three of them set off to explore Myria city.

In the city centre there is an observation tower with excellent views. Zeno and Zormella travel on the turbo-powered elevator to the top of the tower. Zarf doesn't like heights, so he stays behind. How many triangular towers can you see from the top of the observation tower? How many windows are there in each triangular tower?

Zeno and Zormella enjoy looking at the view, but where is Zarf? They look all around, but they cannot find him. Can you see where he is?

In pursuit

Finally Zeno and Zormella spot Zarf. He is speeding away on a number 13 space bus. Zormella recognizes the Numian with him. She has seen him on the news. His name is Moki and he is wanted by the police for kidnapping pet aliens. But where is Moki taking Zarf?

"We should follow them," says Zeno. "Where does the number 13 space bus end its journey?"

WANTED

MOKI

FOR KIDNAPPING EXOTIC PET ALIENS REWARD — 1,000 NUMES

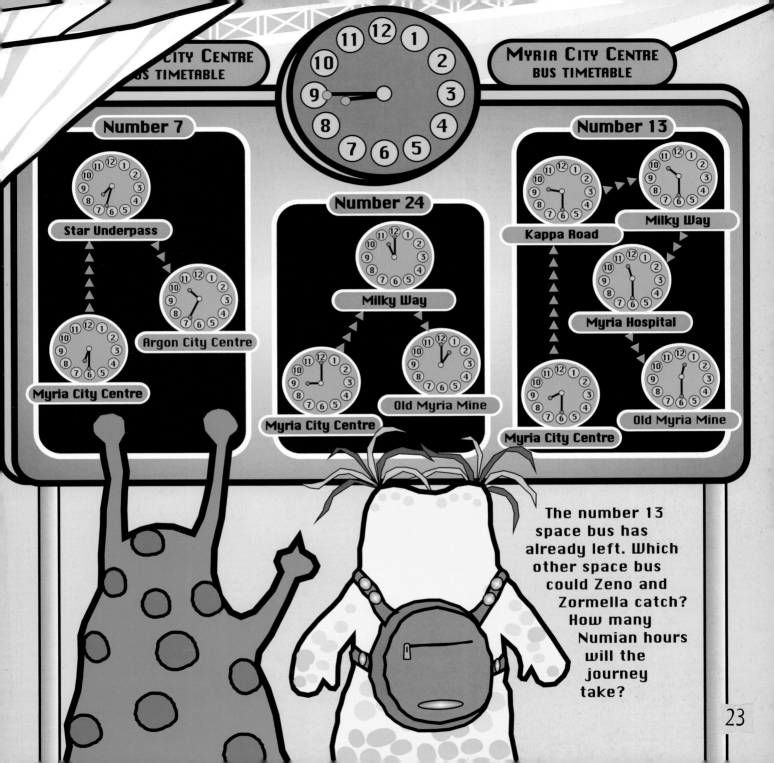

Underground rescue

Zeno and Zormella take the space bus to the Old Myria Mine. At first there is no sign of Zarf or Moki. Then Zormella spots a strange panel by the mine entrance. There are four rows of numbers on the panel. A number is missing from each line. "If we can figure out the missing numbers, maybe we can unlock the gate," suggests Zormella. Can you help?

OLD MYRIA MINE

5	?	15	20	25
2	4	8	?	32
1	4	?	10	13
4	8	12	?	20

Zeno and Zormella type in the code, and the entrance to the old mine opens. It is very dark inside. Luckily Zormella has a torch in her rucksack. In front of them are three tunnels. "Which one should we follow?" asks Zormella. Then Zeno sees a scrap of paper on the ground. The paper has numbers on it. Zarf has left them a clue! Can you figure out which tunnel they should go down?

Escape!

The tunnel leads to a large cave. It is packed with cages full of pet aliens. Zarf is in one of the cages. "Moki must be planning to sell the pets in the next galaxy," whispers Zormella. "That's right!" snarls Moki. He has spotted the two intrepid aliens. "And you won't stop me!"

Zeno notices an empty cage hanging right above Moki. He can trap Moki if he can figure out which lever operates the cage. All he has to do is work out the missing number in the sequence on the cage. Can you help him?

7
14
?
28
35

$6 \times 2 = A$

$A - 5 = B$

$B + 3 =$ Cage release number

It works! With Moki in a cage, Zeno and Zormella can set about freeing the pet aliens and escaping from the mine. To open the cages they need to type the correct number code into the control panel. Can you work out what the code is?

Teatime

Zeno, Zormella and Zarf are happy to be together again, and the pet aliens are very pleased to be rescued. They all take a space bus to Zormella's house. Their exciting day has made them hungry. Zormella's mother has prepared a huge feast for them - parberfish sandwiches, zibber pie and mungo jelly.
"Jumping Jupiter," says Zeno.
"This is delicious!"

Answers

4–5 Testing times

THERE ARE FOUR EMPTY SPACE BUS PODS.
Space buses can only park in square pods. Four green square pods are already in use. There are four square pods with yellow doors.
ZENO CAN DOCK HIS SMALL CRAFT IN FIVE PODS.
As Zeno is flying a small craft, he can only dock in triangle-shaped pods. (Don't forget, an upside-down triangle is still a triangle!) A yellow door shows that a pod is empty. There are five triangle pods with yellow doors.

6–7 On board

Living quarters

IT IS STAR NUMBER 9.
Star number 9 has eight points. All the other stars have six points.

Kitchen

ZENO NEEDS SIX BARP JUICE CARTONS FOR HIS JOURNEY, SO HE DOES HAVE ENOUGH BARP JUICE.
The journey takes 12 hours and Zeno drinks one carton every two hours. There are six 2-hour blocks in 12 hours ($2 \times 6 = 12$ or $2+2+2+2+2+2=12$).

Engine room

THERE ARE NOT ENOUGH IGNITION TUBES LOADED AS ONLY 14 BARS ARE LIT.
Each ignition tube lights up two bars on the display panel and eight ignition tubes are needed. By multiplying 8 by 2 ($8 \times 2 = 16$ or $2+2+2+2+2+2+2+2=16$) you will discover that 16 bars should be lit. Only 14 are lit, so Zeno will need to use one of the spare ignition tubes.

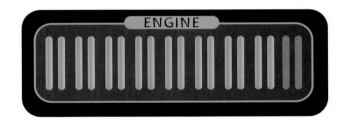

ENGINE

8–9 Take-off

THE MOST POPULAR COLOUR IS ORANGE.
THERE ARE EIGHT BOOSTER ENGINES IN FOUR YELLOW SPACESHIPS.
There are four yellow spaceships and each has two booster engines ($4 \times 2 = 8$ or $2+2+2+2=8$).

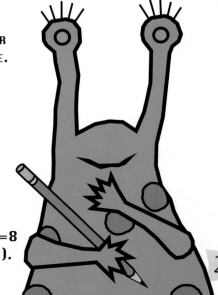

29

Answers

10–11 Fuel stops

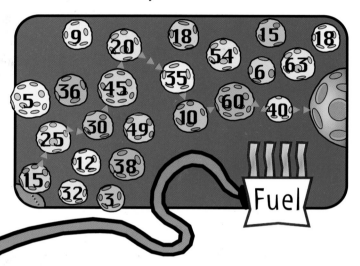

Zeno needs to buy eight fuel packs.
Fuel rods are sold in packs of four and 32 fuel rods are needed. You need to calculate how many fours make up 32 (4×8=32 or 4+4+4+4+4+4+4+4=32).
No, he doesn't need to buy all the fuel packs in the picture.
There are nine fuel packs in the picture and he only needs eight.

12–13 Bubble attack

14+5=19
15–7=8
8–3=5
17–11=6
6+6=12

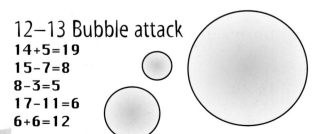

Tip: You may have to try several different sums to use up all the numbers and empty the bubbles.

14–15 Lunchtime

Zeno needs 14 more zibbers.
He's already collected three and the recipe calls for 17.
17–3=14.
There are seven zibbers in each group.
There are 24 zibbers altogether.
There are 3 groups of seven zibbers (3×7=21 or 7+7+7=21), plus the three zibbers already collected (21+3=24).
There are enough space prunes for the recipe.
The recipe needs ten space prunes and there are 16 in the picture.

16–17 Stowaway

Message reads: My name is Zarf.

7+6=13 (M)
5×5=25 (Y)

2×7=14 (N)
10–9=1 (A)
5+8=13 (M)
11–6=5 (E)

3×3=9 (I)
10+9=19 (S)

19+7=26 (Z)
1×1=1 (A)
6×3=18 (R)
2×3=6 (F)

18–19 Planet Numis

FIVE MILLION NUMIANS LIVE IN MYRIA.
Look at the top of the Myria bar and read the scale on the left of the bar chart to see what the population is.
NUMOPOLIS IS THE CITY WITH THE LARGEST POPULATION. SEVEN MILLION NUMIANS LIVE THERE.
The bar for Numopolis is taller than any of the other bars on the bar chart.
PETRUSIUM ORE MINING IS THE BIGGEST INDUSTRY ON PLANET NUMIS.
Petrusium ore mining is the biggest section on the pie chart.

20–21 Sightseeing

THERE ARE SEVEN TRIANGULAR TOWERS.
THERE ARE 30 WINDOWS IN EACH TRIANGULAR TOWER.

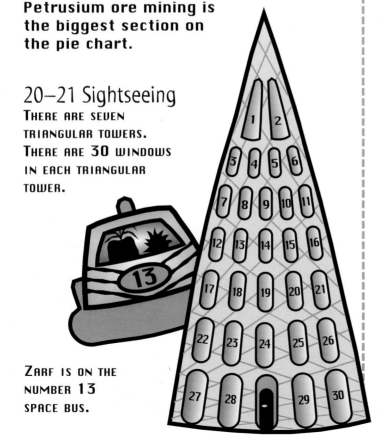

ZARF IS ON THE NUMBER 13 SPACE BUS.

22–23 In pursuit

THE NUMBER 13 SPACE BUS ENDS ITS JOURNEY AT THE OLD MYRIA MINE.
ZENO AND ZORMELLA COULD CATCH THE NUMBER 24 SPACE BUS.
It also goes to the Old Myria Mine and will be leaving in 15 minutes!
THE NUMBER 24 SPACE BUS WILL TAKE FOUR NUMIAN HOURS TO REACH THE OLD MYRIA MINE.

24–25 Underground rescue

THE NUMBERS THEY NEED ARE: **10, 16, 7, 16.**

5 **10** 15 20 25
(The numbers go up in fives)
2 4 8 **16** 24 **(Each number is double the previous number)**
1 4 **7** 10 13 **(Each number is 3 more than previous number)**
4 8 12 **16** 20 **(The numbers go up in fours)**

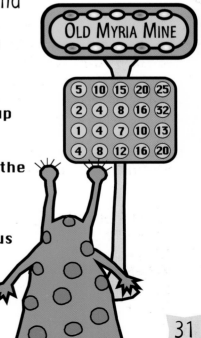

Answers

ZENO AND ZORMELLA SHOULD
GO DOWN TUNNEL 2.
17×2=34
(17+17=34)

26–27 Escape

ZENO SHOULD PULL
THE LEVER NUMBERED
21.
**The numbers go
up in sevens.**
THE CAGE RELEASE
NUMBER
IS 10.
6×2=<u>12</u>
<u>12</u>−5=<u>7</u>
<u>7</u>+3=<u>10</u>

Goodbye!

"It's
time for us
to return to
Mars. I hope
you enjoyed
visiting Zormella as
much as I did. Why not
join us on our next
adventure on Planet Omicron?"